W9-BLJ-224

Jump the Rope Jingles

By EMMA VIETOR WORSTELL

Illustrated by Sheila Greenwald

COLLIER BOOKS, NEW YORK, NEW YORK

COLLIER-MACMILLAN LTD., LONDON

ACKNOWLEDGMENTS

For permission to use the jump rope games indicated grateful acknowledgment is made to the following:

David McKay Company, Inc., for "High Low" from *Fun in the Back Yard* by Arthur Larson and Mary Breen (New York, David McKay Company, Inc., 1954).

Doubleday & Company, Inc., for "Jump the Shot" from *Complete Book of Games* by Clement Wood and Gloria Goddard (Garden City, New York, Doubleday & Company, 1940).

National Recreation Association for "French Almond Rock," "Running In," "Over the Moon," "Salt, Mustard, Vinegar, Pepper," "Steps," "Hot Peas," "All in Together," "Over the Swinging Rope," "Serpents, or over the Waves," "Over and Under," "Higher and Higher," "Double Dutch," and "Keep the Kettle Boiling," from *88 Successful Play Activities*.

Text © 1961 Emma Vietor Worstell. Illustrations © 1961 The Macmillan Company. All rights reserved. No part of this book may be reproduced or transmitted in any form or by any means, electronic or mechanical, including photocopying, recording or by any information storage and retrieval system, without permission in writing from the publisher. The Macmillan Company, 866 Third Avenue, New York, N. Y. 10022. Collier-Macmillan Canada Ltd., Toronto, Ontario. Library of Congress catalog card number: 61–10781. *Jump the Rope Jingles* is also published in a hardcover edition by The Macmillan Company. Printed in the United States of America.

First Collier Books Edition 1972   3 4 5 6/80 79 78 77 76

FOREWORD

As inevitable as the first robin, as inevitable as the waving of dandelions in the winds of spring—just as inevitable is the appearance of jumping ropes on sidewalks and playgrounds throughout our country, when the snow and ice depart.

My mother collected these charming chants, which are half-sung to the tune of the turning rope. Most of them are old as the hills, and they have been handed down from generation to generation. They are used with very little variation from coast to coast.

My two sisters and I contributed a few of the jingles, our young friends added to these, and many came from organized groups throughout the nation. Even visitors to our home responded enthusiastically to Mother's queries on the subject.

The following pages contain the most oft-repeated of these jingles. Mother dedicates them to the children of today.

Greta Marie Worstell

DOWN IN THE VALLEY

Down in the valley where the green grass grows,
There sat (Nancy) as pretty as a rose;
  She sang—she sang,
   She sang so sweet,
Along came (Bunny) and kissed her on the cheek;
How many kisses did he give her in a week?
One, two, three, four *(until jumper misses).*

MARCO POLO

Marco Polo went to France
To teach the ladies how to dance;
First a kick, then a bow,
Marco Polo showed them how.

Marco Polo went to France
To teach the ladies the hootchy-kootchy dance;
Heel, toe, around we go,
Turn your back to the old potato sack!

ALPHABET ROUTINE

My name is Alice, and my
    husband's name is Allen.

And we came from Alabama
    with a carload of apples.

My name is Barbara, and my
    husband's name is Bob.
And we came from Boston
    with a carload of beans.

(Continue through letters of alphabet.)

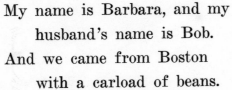

FOUR QUESTIONS

Cinderella, dressed in yeller,
Went downtown to meet her feller.
How many kisses did he give her?
One, two, three, etc.

I like coffee, I like tea
How many boys are crazy for me?
One, two, three, etc.

Bread and butter
Sugar and spice
How many boys think I am nice?
One, two, three, etc.

Sugar and cream
Bread and butter
What is the name of my true lover?
A, B, C, D, etc.
(The last letter a player calls before she misses is her sweetheart's initial.)

KEEP THE POT A-BOILIN'

Keep the pot a-boilin' just for (Marie),
One, two, and a dibble-dabble three.

(When the player's name is called, she
must run in before "three.")

OLD MAN DAISY

Old man Daisy
He went crazy,
Up the ladder,
Down the ladder,
Over my head.

7

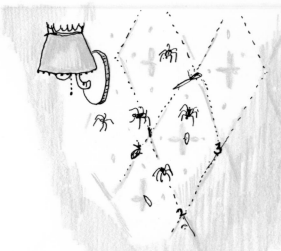

I WOKE UP

I woke up Monday morning,
I gazed upon the wall.
The spiders and the fireflies
Were playing a game of ball;

The score was ten to twelve,
The spiders were ahead;
The fireflies knocked a home run
And knocked me out of bed!

I went downstairs to breakfast,
The bread was hard and stale,
The coffee tasted like tobacco juice
Right out of County Jail.

RICH MAN, POOR MAN

(On the trip of the rope the player discovers occupation of husband-to-be, material used in wedding dress, and where she will live.)

Rich man, poor man, beggarman, thief,
Doctor, lawyer, merchant, chief;
Silk, satin, calico, rags;
Little house, big house, pigpen, barn!

DR. BROWN

Bluebells, cockleshells, evy-ivy-over.
Dr. Brown, a very good man,
Teaches children all he can;
First to read, then to write
Evy-ivy—you run *out!*

HERE COMES THE TEACHER

Here comes the teacher with the big fat stick
    Now get ready for *arithmetic;*
One and one are two—two and two are four;
    Now get ready for *spelling;*
Spell cat c-a-t; spell rat r-a-t;
    Now get ready for *music.*

(Turn PEPPERS [very fast]—Sing "Yankee Doodle"
—then run out.)

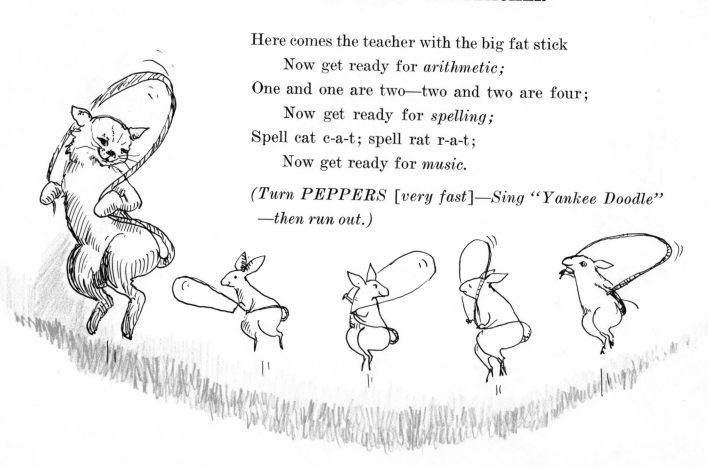

HOW MANY

Grace, Grace, dressed in lace,
Went upstairs to powder her face.
How many boxes of powder did she use?
One, two, three *until player trips on rope.*

Tim, Tim, sat on a pin.
How many inches did it go in?
One, two, three, etc.

Ice cream, soda, ginger ale pop,
Tell me the name of your own sweetheart.
A, B, C, etc.

*(Jump until you come to your sweetheart's first initial, stop,
then jump until you come to his second initial, and so on.)*

ELEVATOR

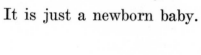

Fudge—Fudge—call the Judge.
Mammy has a newborn baby.
It is not a *girl*,
It is not a *boy*,
It is just a newborn baby.

Wrap it up in tissue paper,
Put it on the elevator.
First floor, miss, second floor, miss, third floor, miss, etc.
(Run out on "sixth floor.")

SPANISH DANCER

Spanish dancer do the splits,
Spanish dancer do high kicks;
Spanish dancer do the kangaroo,
Spanish dancer—out skiddoo!

TILLIE AND BUSTER

Tillie the Toiler sat on a boiler;
The boiler got *hot,*
Tillie got *shot,*
How many times did Tillie get shot?
One, two, three, etc.

Buster, Buster, climb the tree,
Buster, Buster, slap your knee;
Buster, Buster, throw a kiss,
Buster, Buster, do not miss.

ICKY BICKY

My mother and your mother
Live across the street;
Every night they have a fight,
This is what they say:

Icky bicky soda cracker,
    Icky bicky boo,
Icky bicky soda cracker,
    Out goes you.

MABEL

Mabel, Mabel,
Set the table,
Don't forget the
mustard, vinegar, sugar, salt *(on "salt" turn rope slowly)*,
vanilla, cloves (etc.) pepper *(turn rope very fast)*.

OBADIAH

Obadiah
Jumped in the fire.
Fire was so hot, jumped in a pot,
Pot was so little, he jumped in a kettle.
Kettle was so black, he jumped in a crack,
The crack was so high, he jumped to the sky.

Sky was so blue, he jumped in the canoe,
The canoe was so shallow, he jumped in the tallow.
Tallow was so hard, he jumped in the lard,
The lard was so soft, he jumped in the loft.
The loft was so rotten, he fell in the cotton,
The cotton was so white he took off his shoes and
Stayed all night!

MISSES

Miss, Miss, little Miss, Miss.
When she misses, she misses
like this.

(Put your foot over the rope,
or stop rope any other way.)

HOW MANY MILES

Bluebells, cockleshells, evy-ivy-o
My mommy works,
Daddy cuts the meat,
I'm the little meanie who lives across the street.
How many miles do I go?

One, two, three, four *(count until you miss).*

THE THREAD WAS THIN

I went down town an' met Miss Brown,
She gave me a nickel, I bought a pickle,
The pickle was sour, I bought a flower,
The flower was red, I bought some thread,
The thread was thin, I bought a pin,
The pin was sharp, I bought a harp,
And on this harp I played:

Teddy bear, teddy bear, turn around,
Teddy bear, teddy bear, touch the ground;
Teddy bear, teddy bear, show your shoe,
Teddy bear, teddy bear, now skiddoo!

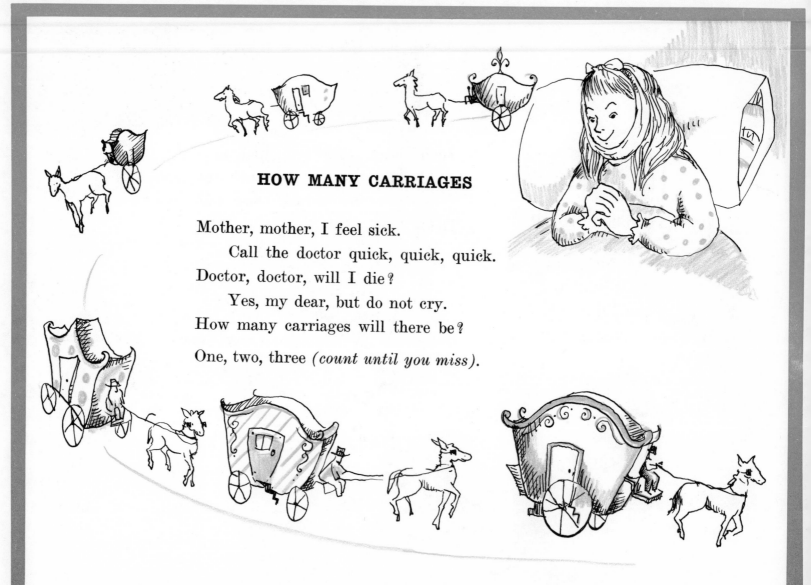

HOW MANY CARRIAGES

Mother, mother, I feel sick.
Call the doctor quick, quick, quick.
Doctor, doctor, will I die?
Yes, my dear, but do not cry.
How many carriages will there be?

One, two, three *(count until you miss)*.

ROOMS FOR RENT

Rooms for rent,
Inquire within,
When I move out,
Let (Anne) move in!

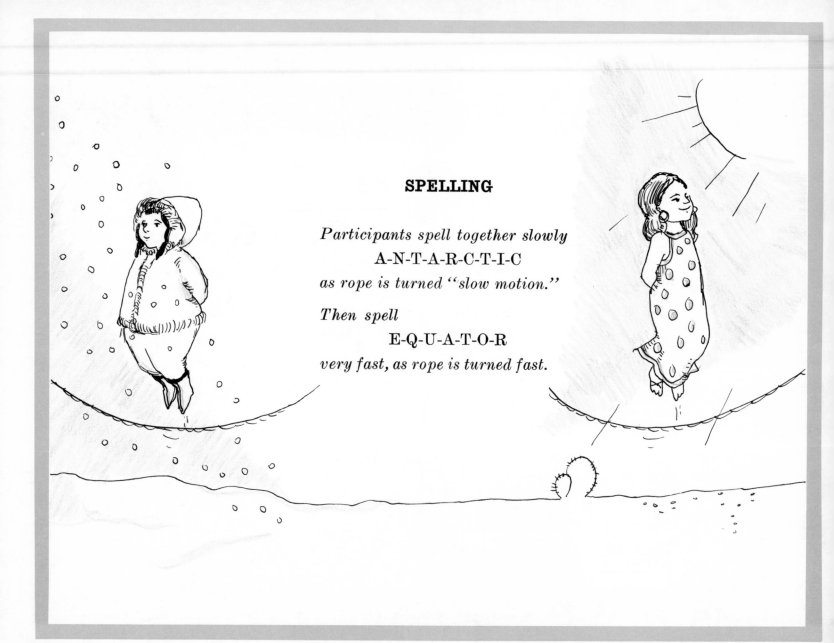

SPELLING

Participants spell together slowly
A-N-T-A-R-C-T-I-C
as rope is turned "slow motion."

Then spell
E-Q-U-A-T-O-R
very fast, as rope is turned fast.

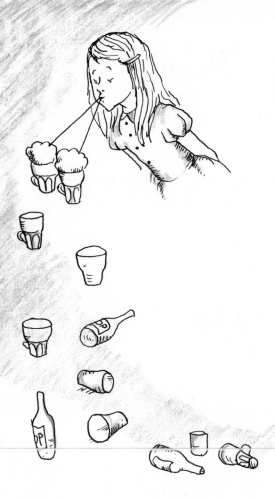

MARGIE

Margie drank some marmalade,
Margie drank some pop,
Margie drank some other things
That made her stomach flop;
Whoops went the marmalade,
Whoops went the pop,
Whoops went the other thing
That made her stomach flop.

O'LEARY

One, two, three *O'Leary*
Four, five, six *O'Leary*
Seven, eight, nine *O'Leary*
Ten O'Leary *more*!

DID YOU EVER?

Did you ever go a-fishing on a sunny day
Sitting on a log—the log rolled away?
Put your hands in your pockets,
Your pockets in your pants,
Did you ever see a fish do the hootchy-kootchy dance?

THE CLOCK

1–Jump once and run out.

2–Jump twice and run out.

3–Jump three times and run out.

4–Jump four times and run out.

5–Jump five times and run out.

6–High waters (rope doesn't touch ground; jump six times).

7–Low waters (rope swings back and forth, without going over head, seven times).

8–Hop eight times.

9–One foot, one eye closed (nine times).

10–Jump ten times with both eyes closed.

11–Cross feet and jump eleven times.

12–Crisscross feet twelve times.

LITTLE DUTCH GIRL

I am a little Dutch Girl
    Dressed in blue;
And these are the things
    I like to do:
Salute to the Captain,
    Bow to the Queen,
And turn my back
    To the submarine!

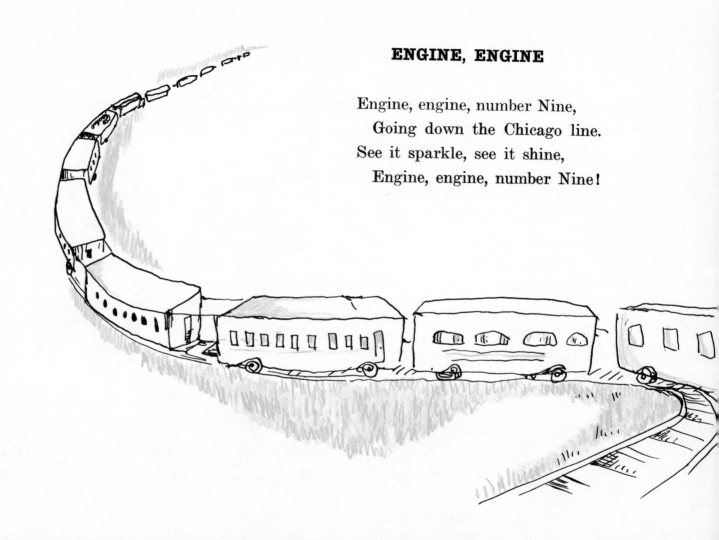

ENGINE, ENGINE

Engine, engine, number Nine,
    Going down the Chicago line.
See it sparkle, see it shine,
    Engine, engine, number Nine!

If the train should jump the track,
    Will I get my money back?
Yes, no, maybe so *(repeating, until jumper*
misses, and if she misses on "no"—no money back).

37

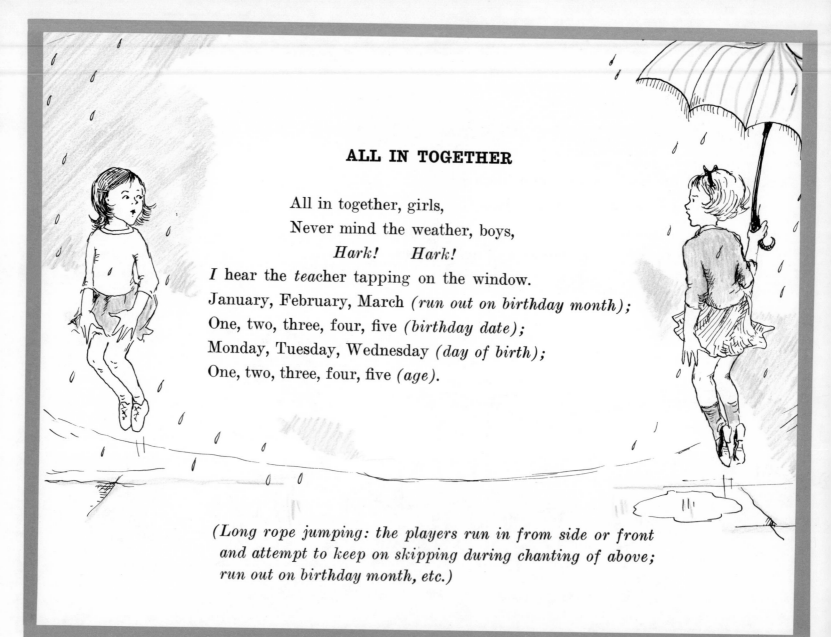

ALL IN TOGETHER

All in together, girls,
Never mind the weather, boys,
    Hark!   *Hark!*
I hear the *tea*cher tapping on the window.
January, February, March *(run out on birthday month)*;
One, two, three, four, five *(birthday date)*;
Monday, Tuesday, Wednesday *(day of birth)*;
One, two, three, four, five *(age)*.

*(Long rope jumping: the players run in from side or front
and attempt to keep on skipping during chanting of above;
run out on birthday month, etc.)*

BOBBY WENT DOWN
TO THE OCEAN

Bobby went down to the ocean,
Bobby went down to the sea,
Bobby broke a milk bottle,
And blamed it onto me;
   I told Ma,
     Ma told Pa,
Bobby got a licking
   Ha, ha, ha!

TEDDY BEAR, TEDDY BEAR

Teddy Bear, Teddy Bear, turn all around,
Teddy Bear, Teddy Bear, touch the ground;

Teddy Bear, Teddy Bear, read the news,
Teddy Bear, Teddy Bear, shine your shoes;

Teddy Bear, Teddy Bear, go upstairs,
Teddy Bear, Teddy Bear, say your prayers;

Teddy Bear, Teddy Bear, turn out the lights,
Teddy Bear, Teddy Bear, say G-O-O-D N-I-G-H-T!

JUMP ROPE GAMES

These are games that you can play with your friends
or by yourself. Some of the games have rhymes in-
cluded, but jingles from the first part of this book
are appropriate to use with those that do not have
their own rhymes. Try several different jingles with
the same game to see which you like best, or vary the
game by sometimes using a new rhyme.

HIGH LOW

One girl or several girls jump as the rope is turned while the rhyme is being sung the first time.

Charley over the water,
Charley over the sea.
Charley caught a blackbird,
But he can't catch *me*.

On the last word they crouch down and the rope is turned over their heads while the rhyme is sung a second time. On the last word the players rise and jump over the rope in the usual fashion while the rhyme is sung a third time. The game is repeated until a fault is made. The fun of this game is leaping up with the changing rhythm of the rope.[1]

INTO THE WALL

While the rope is being turned away from her, the jumper runs in and jumps to an agreed limit, or until she misses.

---

[1] From Arthur Larson and Mary Breen, *Fun in the Back Yard* (New York, David McKay Company, Inc., 1954), pp. 102–103.

CROSS THE CREEK

Players run through without jumping or being touched by the rope—that is, jumpers must get over the creek without getting wet. Players go through separately, until only one is left who has not missed.

ROCK THE BABY

As the rope swings about four inches above the ground, the player jumps from side to side until she misses.

UP THE STAIRS

Jumpers form a single line, jumping over the rope one at a time until all have jumped. When the line forms again, the rope is raised about two or three inches. This is repeated until only one player has not missed.

RED, WHITE AND BLUE

As "Red, white and blue" is chanted, the girl jumps three times. At the next words "stars over you," she stoops and the rope is turned over her head. This may be repeated, or other verses may be added. No one may jump more than fifty verses, and the player jumping most wins.

JUMP THE SHOT

The players form a circle, with room for jumping between them. The player counted out to be IT stands in the center with a 15-foot rope, at whose end a weight is tied, and swings it in a circle until it reaches the players and is moving close to the ground. Each player must jump it as it passes. If the rope or weight touches a player, he is eliminated. The speed of the rope may be changed at will. The IT may stand, sit or lie on the floor for his swinging. The weight may be a bag of beans, an old shoe, or the like.

Variations include the players standing on one foot and hopping, only changing feet when the IT so commands; or running or hopping toward the oncoming rope. Alternately, a bamboo pole may be used instead of a rope.[2]

---

[2] From Clement Wood and Gloria Goddard, *Complete Book of Games* (New York, Garden City, Doubleday & Company, 1940), p. 880.

41

FRENCH ALMOND ROCK

The players jump over the rope as it swings from side to side, saying the following rhyme: "Handy-pandy, sugardy candy, French almond rock." Then the rhyme is repeated while the players skip in the usual way. Then all crouch down while the rope is turned over their heads, to the same rhyme. On the last word, "rock," the players rise and the rhyme is repeated for the third time while they skip. The process may be repeated, or the first set of skippers run out and a new set begin.[3]

RUNNING IN

The children, in groups of five or more, run in from a little distance, and then after a certain number of skips, out again without checking the rope.[3]

OVER THE MOON

Both the preceding games can be taken with the rope turned backward.[3]

---

[3] From National Recreation Association, New York, *88 Successful Play Activities*, pp. 44–45.

42

"SALT, MUSTARD, VINEGAR, PEPPER"

The children run in, and when all are in they say, "Salt, Mustard, Vinegar, Pepper." At the word "Pepper," the rope is gradually turned faster and faster.[3]

STEPS

The ropes are arranged in increasing heights.[3]

HOT PEAS

Turn the rope as fast as possible. Spell H-O-T-S and at the end of that begin counting 1-2-3, etc., and turn fast at the beginning of the count. The girl jumping most wins.[3]

ALL IN TOGETHER

As the name implies, the children enter as quickly as they can and try to continue skipping until all are in. As soon as the last player enters, count is kept of the number of skips that are kept up.
(Note: The easiest way to enter is from the side.)[3]

OVER THE SWINGING ROPE

The ropes, arranged as in "Keep the Kettle Boiling" [see page 43], are swung slowly from side to side, and the players must judge their jumps accordingly. Later the difficulty may be increased by changing the rate of the swing.[3]

SERPENTS, OR OVER THE WAVES

Waves are made in the ropes by one turner at each end moving his arm upward and downward, slowly or quickly at will. Players jump over the ropes, watching carefully, as the height and speed of the waves will probably be different at each rope.[3]

HIGHER AND HIGHER

The rope is turned so that it does not quite touch the ground and is very gradually raised so that the players must jump or lift their knees higher and higher to clear it.[3]

DOUBLE DUTCH

Two ropes are used. The turners have a rope in each hand; they hold their arms rather far apart and make the ropes touch the ground alternately. The ropes may be turned either inward or outward.[3]

OVER AND UNDER

The players jump over one rope and crawl under the next.[3]

KEEP THE KETTLE BOILING

Ropes are placed at suitable intervals around the playground or radiate from the center. The players form in twos, threes, or fours, and at a signal all run round the course, jumping each rope in turn. The object of the game is to keep the jumping continuous; the ropes should therefore be quite low at first. Later they may be raised slightly, but they should be adjusted to the capacity of the weakest jumper.[3]

Here are some jump rope games for a player turning her own rope:

SPREAD EAGLE: Stand with the feet spread and jump with or without an intervening hop.

SINGLE JUMP: Jump rope with no intervening hop, keeping both feet together.

DOUBLE JUMP: Jump rope every other time it passes, with both feet together. There is an intervening hop.

RUNNING: Run in place with no hop between the steps. Step over the rope each time a foot is raised, alternating left and right.

CROSS-FOOT: Jump rope with the feet crossed, changing the position of the feet on each jump.

SKIPPING: Stand on the right foot, hop on the right foot and let the rope go under; step on the left foot, hop on the left foot and pass the rope under. Then repeat on the right foot and continue alternating.

BUCK AND WING: Click the heels together between jumps.

JUMP BACKWARD: Swing rope backward under the feet. Any jumping method may be used.

CLICK HANDLES: Each time the rope is jumped, click the handles of the rope together.

ONE LEG SKIP: Hold one leg off the pavement and skip on the other foot.

STIFF-LEG KICK: Jump the rope first with one foot and then with the other, throwing the raised leg forward on each skip and keeping the knee stiff.

43

INDEX OF FIRST LINES